D0363474

£5.99
UK only

Disney's
Princess invites

(your name)

into a magical world, where you can become a princess with Belle, Pocahontas, Cinderella, Ariel, Jasmine, Sleeping Beauty and Mulan.

Belle

Pocahontas

Cinderella

Ariel

Jasmine

Sleeping Beauty

Mulan

Competition!

Now turn the page to begin the fairy-tale...

Belle's Party

1 Belle had agreed to live in the Beast's castle. She was getting used to her new life and on warm, sunny days she loved to walk in the castle grounds.

2 The Beast was growing fond of Belle. One morning he joined her on her walk. "I have a special present for you," he said, shyly.

3 "A present! How lovely!" said Belle. "I love presents – and parties. My father and I used to have wonderful parties with our friends. I remember…"

4 But the Beast had gone. "What's wrong? What have I said?" wondered Belle. "Wait!" she called, rushing after him.

5 Belle couldn't catch up with the Beast, so she went to look for her friends. "Whatever's the matter my dear?" asked Mrs Potts, kindly.

6 Belle told them what had happened. "I don't think the master has ever had a party," sighed Lumiere. Belle could hardly believe it.

7 Then she had an idea. "Let's give him a surprise party!" "Fantastic!" cried Lumiere.

8 Soon, everyone was very busy! In the kitchen, they made jellies and cakes. "You can't come in – the kitchen's being cleaned!" Cogsworth told the Beast.

9 "And the library is being er... er... dusted," Lumiere said, stopping the Beast from seeing his presents being wrapped.

10 Just as the final decorations were being hung in the ballroom, the Beast appeared at the door. "The floor is being polished!" giggled Belle.

11 The Beast felt sad and lonely. He thought his friends didn't want to see him.

12 "Well done!" said Belle, when everything was ready. "Now all we need is the guest of honour!"

13 Belle searched all over the castle for the Beast. At last she found him.

14 "Go away," he growled. "Don't be grumpy," said Belle. "I've got something to show you. Follow me."

15 Belle led the Beast into the ballroom. "Surprise!" shouted all their friends. "Welcome to your party," smiled Belle. The Beast couldn't believe his eyes.

16 "I'm sorry I've been horrible," said the Beast. "I was jealous because I've never had a party. Please forgive me and accept this." "I understand," smiled Belle, taking the gift.

17 When Belle lifted the lid, she gasped. Inside was a beautiful tiara. "Oh! Thank you!" she cried, putting her arms around the Beast. How everyone cheered!

THE END

Enchanting

Belle and the Beast are dancing by moonlight.
One of Belle's special friends is hiding on
the terrace. Who is it?

How many stars you can see in the sky?

Four things are wrong in the picture.
Can you find them?

Dazzling!

Look just like beautiful Belle by making your very own sparkling golden tiara.

1 Cut out a strip of gold card that is long enough to go around your head and is slightly thicker at the centre.

3 Push a bead on to the end of each cocktail stick. Hold them in place with glue if necessary.

4 Glue the cocktail sticks on to the back of the thicker section of the card, so they make a pretty shape.

You will need:

scissors

cocktail sticks

glue

gold paint

fake jewels

gold paper

paintbrush

beads

2 Ask an adult to cut the sharp ends off the cocktail sticks, then to cut them to different lengths. Paint them gold.

5 Finally, make your tiara really sparkle by gluing on fake jewels.

A Date for Dinner

Belle is having a magical dinner with the Beast.
Are there more knives or forks on the table?

Which of these items doesn't
appear in the picture?

a

b

c

Use Lumiere's code
to read what's on
Cogsworth's menu.

How many matching
pairs of glasses are there?

How many differences
can you find between the
two cakes on the table?

m ◆ ◻ ⽊
a b c e
♋ 〰 ● ♌
f k o p
✦ ⊠ ⌘ ◻
s u n

15

The Dream Catcher

1 One night as Pocahontas slept, she began to have a wonderful dream. In the dream she danced with her special friend, John Smith.

2 But suddenly, Pocahontas's dream turned into a nightmare. Men with guns were chasing her.

3 Pocahontas was so frightened that she woke up with a jump. She felt too scared to go back to sleep.

4 Next day, Pocahontas told Grandmother Willow about her dream. "It started nicely and made me feel happy. But then it turned scary," she said.

5 "You need a dream catcher," said Grandmother Willow. "A dream catcher?" asked Pocahontas.

6 Grandmother Willow sent Pocahontas to find a supple twig, a strong vine and a feather. Then she told Pocahontas how to make a dream catcher.

7 While Pocahontas worked, Meeko went looking for food. When he tried to pick a spiky fruit, the prickles hurt his paw.

8 Soon, Pocahontas finished. "Hang it above your bed," said Grandmother Willow. "It will trap bad dreams and let good ones through."

9 That night, Pocahontas brought the dream catcher to her tepee. When Meeko saw it, he thought it was some food!

10 Meeko soon lost interest in the dream catcher and he snuggled down to sleep.

11 Pocahontas carefully tied the dream catcher from the centre of the tepee. It was hanging right over her bed.

12 But Pocahontas still couldn't sleep. "What if the dream catcher doesn't work and I have another nightmare?" she thought.

13 Pocahontas noticed that Meeko was restless. He was having a bad dream about the prickly fruit that hurt his paw.

14 Suddenly, a real prickly fruit dropped through the top of the tepee. It was falling straight towards Meeko!

15 But the fruit got caught on the dream catcher and split open. The juice dripped into Meeko's mouth and his nightmare turned into a lovely dream.

16 "If the dream catcher worked that well for Meeko, then I'm sure it will work for me," thought Pocahontas, and she finally dropped off to sleep.

THE END

Forest Fun

Pocahontas is exploring with her friends, Meeko and Flit.

How many butterflies can you see? Which two are the same?

If Meeko started with nine biscuits, how many has he eaten?

b
c
d
e

Help Pocahontas put the feathers in order of size, starting with the smallest.

20

Charming Changes

Meeko and Flit are plaiting Pocahontas's hair.
Can you find six differences in the bottom picture?

21

Princess

Have a go at making this colourful plaited headband – it's fit for a princess!

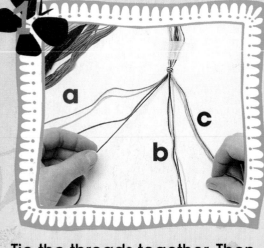

Tie the threads together. Then divide them into three groups, each one with four threads.

Take the threads on the right, **c**, and put them over the threads in the middle, **b**.

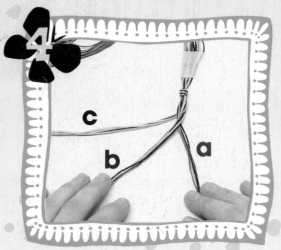

Now take threads **b** and put them over threads **a**. You should see a plait forming.

Keep plaiting in the same way. When you get near the end, tie a knot in the threads.

Plaits

Princess tip!

Try tucking some feathers in your headband for a real princess look!

You will need:

12 lengths of embroidery thread, 150cm long

tape   beads

Then take the threads on the left, **a**, and put them into the middle, over threads **c**.

Make a matching bracelet, too!

Thread beads on to each end of your headband. Hold them in place with knots.

23

The Special Hat

Cinderella's stepmother had asked an artist to paint a portrait of the family and Cinderella was determined not to wear her rags...

Cinderella had been working hard and had made herself a lovely new dress.

"Now all I have to do is make a hat!" she said.

Cinderella worked quickly and soon finished the hat, too.

"I'd better feed the chickens," she said. "If I don't finish my chores, I won't be allowed to have my portrait painted."

While she was outside, her stepsister, Drizella, came into the kitchen and saw the hat.

"I'll look lovely wearing this in the portrait," she said, and took it!

When Cinderella returned and saw that the hat was missing, she set to work to make another one. Just as she finished, the kitchen bell rang. It was her stepmother wanting her tea.

"Coming!" cried Cinderella.

This time, as soon as Cinderella was gone, her other stepsister, Anastasia, crept in and took the second hat!

"This will make me look the best in the portrait!" she said.

So, poor Cinderella had to make yet another hat.

"That's pretty!" said her stepmother, watching her work. "It's a pity there are still chores to do and you won't have time to have your portrait painted. But the hat won't go to waste – I'll wear it!"

"But the hat is not meant for you!" cried Cinderella.

But it was too late, her stepmother had gone. Cinderella's mouse friends felt so sorry for her, they helped to make yet another hat, and to finish her chores.

When all the work was done, Cinderella put on her new dress. Then she picked up the hat and put it on... the horse!

"I promised I'd make you a hat, so here it is," said Cinderella. "In fact, you look so lovely," she added, "I think you should come and have your portrait painted, too!"

Outside, Cinderella's stepmother and sisters were so busy fighting over their identical hats, they didn't notice that the artist was already painting them, or that Cinderella and the horse were behind them!

Imagine their surprise when they saw the finished painting!

"There's a horse wearing a hat just like ours!" Cinderella's stepmother screamed!

Cinderella couldn't help but smile at the very silly painting!

*Make a glittering ball mas
and be a mystery princess.*

1

Draw a mask shape on to
pink card and cut it out.
Glue it on to blue card and
draw a larger mask shape
around it. Cut it out.

2

Hold your mask up to your
face and ask someone to
draw a dot where your
eyes are. Carefully cut
two eye holes.

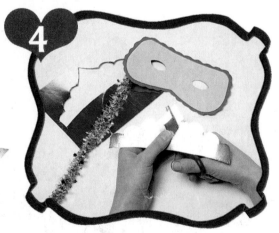

4

Draw a tiara to fit your mask
on to shiny card and cut it
out. Cut holes in it.

Ball Mask

3

Wrap tinsel around the plant stick. Hold it in place with sticky tape. Attach the stick to the back of the mask at one side.

Princess tip!
You can make your mask any shape you like.

5

Glue the tiara on to the mask, then decorate it with tinsel, fake jewels and ribbons.

It's Magical!

These pictures show the story of how Cinderella's fairy godmother turned her rags into a ball gown. Can you put them in the right order?

1

2

3

4

5

6

Answers: 4,3,2,6,1,5.

A Wish Come True!

Cinderella has to return from the ball at midnight.
Which clock shows that time?

Which shadow matches the coach and horses?

Answers:
Clock 3 • Shadow a.

29

The Sunken Village

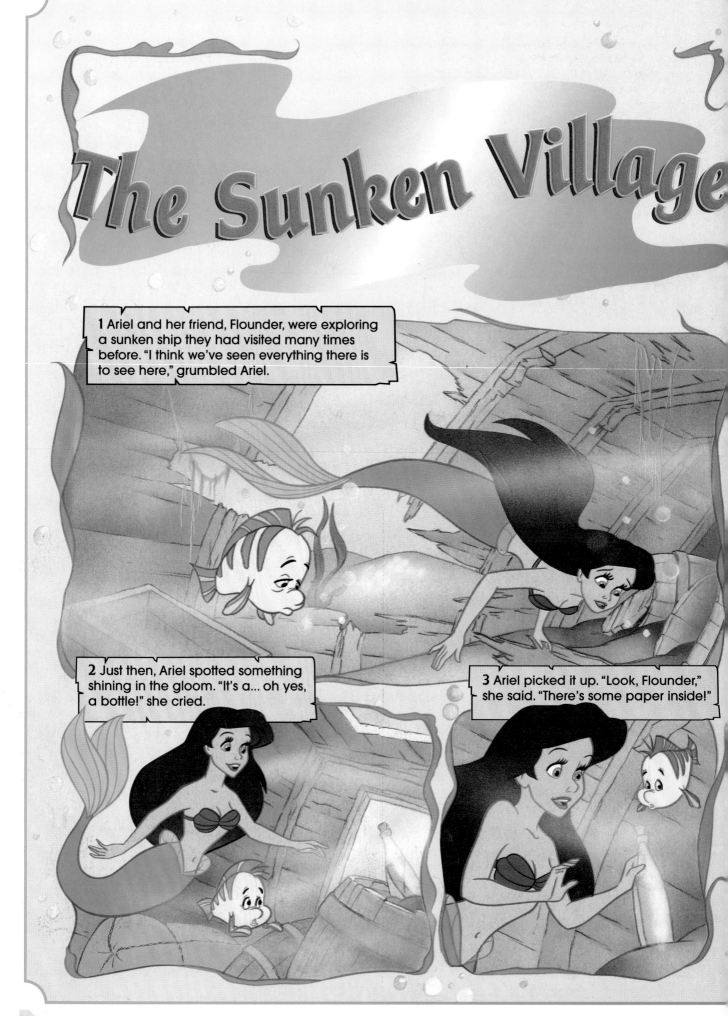

1 Ariel and her friend, Flounder, were exploring a sunken ship they had visited many times before. "I think we've seen everything there is to see here," grumbled Ariel.

2 Just then, Ariel spotted something shining in the gloom. "It's a... oh yes, a bottle!" she cried.

3 Ariel picked it up. "Look, Flounder," she said. "There's some paper inside!"

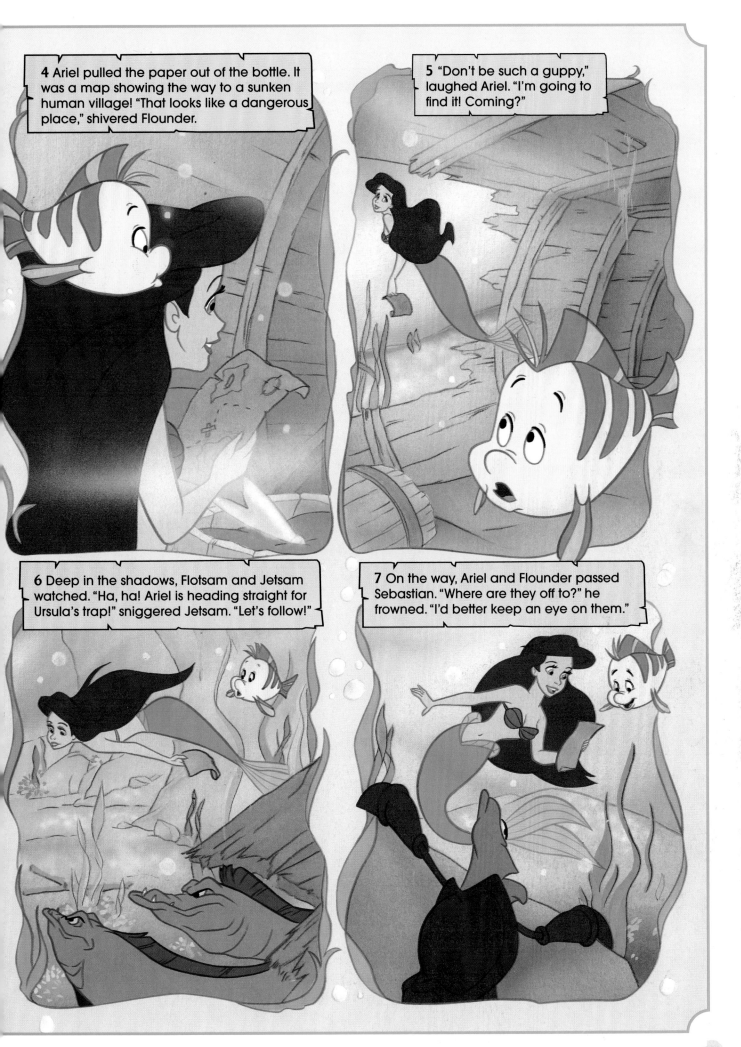

4 Ariel pulled the paper out of the bottle. It was a map showing the way to a sunken human village! "That looks like a dangerous place," shivered Flounder.

5 "Don't be such a guppy," laughed Ariel. "I'm going to find it! Coming?"

6 Deep in the shadows, Flotsam and Jetsam watched. "Ha, ha! Ariel is heading straight for Ursula's trap!" sniggered Jetsam. "Let's follow!"

7 On the way, Ariel and Flounder passed Sebastian. "Where are they off to?" he frowned. "I'd better keep an eye on them."

8 Ariel followed the map carefully and soon they found the village. "Oh Flounder, it's wonderful," she grinned. "Let's look inside a house."

9 Ariel didn't notice the eels lurking at the door. "I haven't got one of these," she said, picking up a bottle of ink.

10 In her lair, Ursula watched in her crystal ball. She grinned as the eels slammed shut the door of the house.

11 "Ursula will set you free, Ariel," sniggered Jetsam. "But only if you give her your lovely voice!" grinned Flotsam.

12 "Huh, we'll see about that," muttered Ariel, trying to escape up the chimney. But it wasn't big enough.

13 "Oh Ariel, what a mess!" said Sebastian, suddenly appearing. "Sebastian!" gasped Ariel. "Have you been following us?"

14 "Hang on!" said Ariel. "You'll fit up the chimney. Go and turn the key-thing, while Flounder distracts the eels!"

15 "Yah-boo!" Flounder shouted through the window. "Hey, squid-face! Slug-nose!"

16 The eels were so furious, they didn't see Sebastian sneak past.

17 Sebastian quickly unlocked the door and Ariel and Flounder swam out. "Watch out! Here come the eels," he shouted.

18 Ariel took the lid off the bottle of ink. "This should give us time to escape," she grinned.

19 A cloud of ink swamped the eels and gave the friends time to swim safely home.

20 "I want you to promise never to go there again," said Sebastian. But Ariel had enjoyed the adventure. "Well, not today anyway!" she chuckled to herself.

THE END

Underwater World

Ariel lives in a beautiful world under the sea.
Flounder is hiding in the picture.
Can you find him?

1 2 3 4 5 7 6

O H D I
L   N P

Carefully follow each piece
of seaweed to spell out the
name of a sea creature.

Which of these fish isn't in the picture?

a   b   c

Treasure

If you like collecting things, like Ariel, make a treasure chest for your trinkets.

1 Cover your box in blue paper, then carefully cut a hole in the top.

2 Cut two card semicircles to fit the sides of the box. Bend card over the top and hold in place with tape.

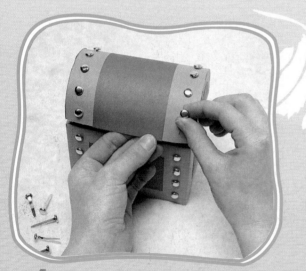

4 Decorate by carefully pushing paper fasteners through the box and lid.

5 Finally, glue on squares of darker paper and a lock cut out of gold card.

Secrets

Princess tip!
Draw a pretty pattern on the gold lock using a pencil.

You will need:

card

coloured paper

scissors

sticky tape

box

paper fasteners

glue

3 Cover the lid with blue paper, then attach it to the back of the box with sticky tape.

Princess Ariel is going to draw Flounder.
Follow these four easy steps to draw
your own picture of her cute friend.

1

2

Painting

3

4

Here are some more fish shapes for you to copy and add to your picture.

The Unwanted Guests

Princess Jasmine was often visited by horrible princes who wanted to marry her. If only she could find a way of avoiding them...

One day, while Jasmine was in the palace gardens, she heard a commotion at the gates.

"Oh no, it's *another* prince!" sighed Jasmine. "They only want to marry me for my father's wealth. Quick Rajah – let's hide."

So Jasmine hid behind a tree, and Rajah amongst some grasses.

Jasmine's father, the Sultan, couldn't see her anywhere.

"It seems your visit has been a wasted one!" he told the prince.

But at that very moment, the prince spotted Jasmine's sleeve poking out from behind the tree.

"Ah, here you are. What about a kiss for your future husband?" said the prince.

Quickly, Rajah leapt out of his hiding place and growled. The prince was terrified and ran screaming from the palace!

"Your stripes almost made you disappear in those grasses," said Jasmine to Rajah. "I wish I could hide that well!"

Then Jasmine had an idea! Later that day, when another prince came to visit, Jasmine draped herself in some green,

searched high and low.

Just then, he noticed a pair of eyes staring out of the grasses.

"Ah, there you are!" he cried. "I hope you won't be this hard to find when we're married!"

With that, he leant forward and kissed... Rajah!

"Ahhh," he cried as he ran from the palace. "I've kissed a tiger!"

When he was gone, Jasmine stepped out of her hiding place.

"Thanks to you it looks as if I've finally found a way of avoiding all those unwanted guests!" she laughed, giving Rajah a big hug!

patterned material and hid behind a bush. Now she was better hidden, just like Rajah.

"You can see that Jasmine isn't here," said the Sultan to the prince.

But the prince was determined to find her and he began looking behind all the trees and bushes.

"I know you're here, Princess Jasmine!" he called out as he

Princess Presents

Princess Jasmine is in the palace gardens with Aladdin and Rajah. Can you find Magic Carpet in the picture, too?

fra cs

Aladdin has brought Jasmine three gifts that she can wear. Unscramble the letters on the boxes to find out what they are.

Cheeky Abu has taken five items out of Jasmine's jewellery box and left them outside! Can you find them?

Are there more doves flying or walking?

43

Golden Bracelet

Every princess loves glamorous jewellery. So, why not make a beautiful bracelet, like Jasmine's?

You will need:

- scissors
- gold paint
- thin card
- paintbrush
- glitter glue
- glue
- string
- fake jewels

1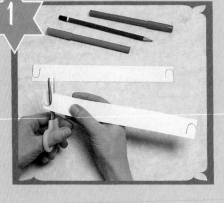

Cut out a strip of card long enough to go loosely around your wrist. Cut a curved slot at each end of the card as shown.

2

Glue some string in swirly patterns on one side of the card.

Cover the string and the card with gold paint, then leave to dry.

3

4

Decorate your bracelet with fake jewels or glitter glue. Slot the ends together to wear your bracelet.

You'll look stunning in your jewelled bracelet.

Perfect Princess

Princess Jasmine is in her room at the Sultan's palace.
How many pairs of shoes has she got?

Which of these objects isn't in Jasmine's bedroom?

Which vase matches the one in the picture?

45

A New Dress for Briar Rose

1 Briar Rose had been in her bedroom all morning, looking at books. Her aunts could hear happy singing, but they didn't know what she was doing.

2 "I thought I might make myself a dress," said Briar Rose, excitedly. "I've been looking through books for ideas – but I just can't decide."

3 "You'd look lovely in a blue dress with ribbons," said Merryweather.

4 "No, a pink one with lace would suit you better," interrupted Flora.

5 "But blue will match your eyes," said Merryweather. "And pink will bring out the colour in your cheeks," said Flora.

6 "You're confusing Briar Rose!" cried Fauna. "I'm afraid you are," said Briar Rose. "I'll go for a walk to clear my head."

7 Briar Rose wandered into the wood and as usual, her special friends, the forest animals came to greet her.

8 "I can't make up my mind what kind of dress I want!" Briar Rose told the animals. "And no-one seems to be able to help me."

9 "And I'm so tired," she yawned. "Maybe I'll dream of a dress – they say that if you dream of something more than once, it will come true!"

10 Soon, Briar Rose was fast asleep. As she slept, leaves from the trees started to fall around her. This gave the owl an idea, which he told to the others.

11 Soon, the birds had collected long grasses, the squirrel and rabbits had picked daisies and the owl had collected leaves.

12 Quickly, they set to work. The birds started to weave a dress using the grass.

13 The owl carefully added leaves to the dress.

14 Then the squirrel decorated it with a string of daisies.

15 Finally, one of the rabbits hopped over and gave the owl a beautiful pink rose to finish off the dress.

16 At that moment, Briar Rose woke up and saw the dress. "It's beautiful," she gasped. "No-one else could make one like this – wearing it will make me feel like a princess!"

THE END

Woodland Walk

Briar Rose is picking berries in the wood.

Can you name the animals in the picture?
How many of each kind can you see?

Which jigsaw piece completes the picture?

a

b

c

d

Can you work out which bird is tugging at which worm?

Mystery Meeting

Make sure that Briar Rose gets to meet Prince Phillip
by helping him find the way across the river.

Mulan and the Matchmaker

Many years ago, in China, there was a girl called Mulan who longed to bring honour to her family.

One of the ways Mulan could bring honour to her family was to make a good match in marriage. So, when the day came for her to meet the Matchmaker, she was nervous. She wanted to make a good impression.

But, as usual, Mulan was late! She rushed around, feeding the chickens and taking tea to her father. Then she leapt on her horse, Khan, and rode to meet her mother, Fa Li.

By the time Mulan got to town, her hair was tangled and she was covered in dust. Mulan needed to be smartened up before she could go to the special meeting.

Mulan's hair was washed and combed and she was dressed in beautiful silks. Her mother even gave her a special comb to wear in her hair.

Finally, her grandmother gave her a cricket, called Cri-Kee, for good luck.

Although Mulan felt very uncomfortable in her fine clothes, she looked beautiful.

But Mulan's meeting with the Matchmaker soon started to go very wrong.

Cri-Kee escaped from his cage and took a swim in the Matchmaker's tea! Mulan had to grab the cup to stop the Matchmaker from swallowing the cheeky cricket! This made the Matchmaker jump back in surprise and set her clothes alight on the stove!

Quickly, Mulan threw the pot of tea over the Matchmaker to put out the flames. The Matchmaker wasn't on fire anymore, but she was furious!

"You will never bring your family honour!" she shouted.

Mulan was sad. She felt as if she had disgraced her family. But her father, Fa Zhou, knew she had meant no harm.

"This blossom is late," he said, pointing at a bud on a tree in the garden. "But I'll bet that when it blooms it will be the most beautiful of all."

Mulan smiled. She knew her father was telling her that one day, she too would blossom and bring honour to her family.

Mulan's Mirror

Make Mulan's lovely mirror –

it's fit for a princess!

You will need:

silver card
gold paper

card

glue

scissors

gold string

Tie a tassel on to your mirror, too!

1 Draw and cut out two identical mirror shapes, one on white card, one on black. Carefully cut a hole in the middle of the black mirror.

Cut out a small piece of silver card and glue it on to the other mirror shape. Glue the black mirror on top.

2

3

Wind gold string around the handle. Glue it in place on the back of the mirror. Finally, decorate by sticking on pieces of gold paper.

Dressing-up!

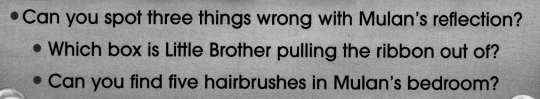

- Can you spot three things wrong with Mulan's reflection?

- Which box is Little Brother pulling the ribbon out of?

- Can you find five hairbrushes in Mulan's bedroom?

Fluttering

Mulan has drawn a beautiful butterfly. Have a go at drawing one, too, then follow these steps to find out how to make it flutter as it flies.

When you throw your butterfly into the air, it will flutter to the ground.

Butterfly

You will need:

felt-tipped pens

paper

Plasticine

scissors

pencil

1 Trace the butterfly on to paper. Go over the lines in black pen, then cut it out. Colour it in on both sides.

2 Fold the edge of one wing towards you, and the edge of the other wing away from you.

3 Press a small piece of Plasticine on to your butterfly's tail. Now throw your butterfly into the air.

Like a Princess

Have you ever wondered which princess you are most like? Play this game to find out. All you need is a counter.

START

Do you follow the latest fashions?

YES — Do you love cute animals?

Do you prefer being outside to inside?

YES

YES — Do you like sewing?

NO

Do you like singing?

NO — Do you help around the house?

NO — Do you enjoy playing sports?

YES

YES / NO

Are you good at following instructions?

NO

Do you love reading?

Are you neat and tidy?

YES

NO — YES

YES — Sleeping Beauty

Belle

Cinderella

Mulan

How to Play: Place your counter at the start. Answer the question, then follow the correct arrow to move your counter to the next question. Continue until you reach a princess. You are most like this princess.

Are you always looking for adventure?

YES → Do you like dancing?

YES → Do you like collecting things?

YES → NO

NO → Are you a day-dreamer?

NO → Do you mind getting messy?

YES

NO → Do you love swimming?

NO

NO → Do you prefer pastel colours to bright colours?

YES → Do you prefer big pets to small ones?

NO → Are you always on time?

YES

YES → NO

YES → NO

YES

YES → NO

Pocahontas

Jasmine

Ariel

Come see Disney's Millennium Celebrations

Win!   **Win!**

2000
at Walt Disney World. Resort
IN FLORIDA

Win a fantastic holiday to Walt Disney World® Resort in Florida!

There is an amazing party to celebrate the Millennium, starting on 1st October 1999 for 15 months at EPCOT®. Enter this competition to make sure you're in with a chance of joining in with all the fun!

You'll get to meet all your favourite Disney characters and there will be fantastic shows with lasers, fireworks, special effects and much, much more.

As well as **EPCOT**® you'll be able to visit Walt Disney World's other Theme Parks: **The Magic Kingdom**® Park, **Disney-MGM Studios, Disney's Animal Kingdom®** Theme Park and Disney's three wonderful **water parks**. It's a Disney dream come true!

The Prize:

7 nights accommodation at a Walt Disney World® Resort Hotel for a family of 4 (one room for the winning family) and free entry to all 4 Walt Disney World® Theme Parks and 3 water parks. Prize includes return economy flights from Manchester or Gatwick to Orlando International or Sanford Airport. Meals are not included.

Send your answer, along with your name and address to:

Egmont World Ltd,
Deanway Technology Centre,
Wilmslow Road,
Handforth,
Cheshire SK9 3FB.

How to enter:

Unscramble these letters to spell out a very famous Disney character: KIMCEY

The closing date for entries is the 14th January 2000.

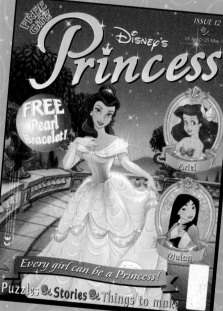